Mental Maths

Daily Workout 1

Peter Patilla & Paul Broadbent

Addison Wesley Longman
Edinburgh Gate,
Harlow, Essex,
CM20 2JE,

England and Associated Companies throughout the World.

First published 1997

© Addison Wesley Longman 1997

The right of Peter Patilla and Paul Broadbent to be identified as the authors of this Work has been asserted by them in accordance with the Copyright, Designs and Patents Act of 1988.

Designed by Ken Vail Graphic Design, Cambridge.

Printed in Singapore

ISBN   0 582 30355 9

Introduction

Mental Maths Daily Workout is a series of books for pupils aged 6–11.

Book 1 for pupils aged 6–7 in Year 2/P2.

Book 2 for pupils aged 7–8 in Year 3/P3.

Book 3 for pupils aged 8–9 in Year 4/P4.

Book 4 for pupils aged 9–10 in Year 5/P5.

Book 5 for pupils aged 10–11 in Year 6/P6.

Mental Maths Daily Workout contains two types of mental activities:

■ ORAL maths where the questions and responses are verbal.

■ MENTAL maths where the questions and answers are written but the calculation should occur in the head.

Each double page showing ORAL and MENTAL activities represents approximately one week's work for about 15 minutes each day.

ORAL Maths

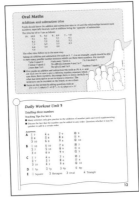

■ The ORAL maths activities have been designed as a whole class activity.

■ Each unit's ORAL activities represents approximately one week's work for approximately 5–10 minutes each day and has a clearly stated purpose.

■ The ORAL activities develop skills independent of that unit's MENTAL activities. Many of the skills are applied later in the MENTAL work.

■ The resource sheets on pages 62–64 are needed for some of the ORAL maths activities.

■ Many of the activities include 'Show me' problems where pupils hold up different types of Number Cards in response to the questions. This avoids the problem of some pupils calling out the answer and of others not taking part.

MENTAL Maths

■ Each week's MENTAL maths activities have been written in five sets. Each set should take less than 10 minutes to complete.

■ Set A has a clear focus to the questions and can be used as a teaching point or checkpoint.

■ Set B contains a range of sums to be answered mentally, with no words being used in the questions.

■ Set C contains a range of word sums to check that mathematical vocabulary is understood.

■ Set D contains problems which will require more interpretation and understanding. They often require more than one operation to solve them.

■ Set E is the section which checks that pupils can remember and recall a range of mathematical facts, names and operations. This set also re-visits the focus from previous units.

■ The questions can be read out orally for pupils to record their answers or pupils can write their answers on the question sheet itself.

Record Sheets

Two record sheets are provided on pages 60 and 61. The Mental Maths Record Sheet on page 60 provides teachers with a chart for recording the date a particular unit was completed and any appropriate notes. The Mental Maths Pupil Record Sheet on page 61 allows a pupil to keep a record of the sheets completed and, if required, a score for each set in a unit.

These ORAL and MENTAL activities have been deliberately written as closed activities to complement more open investigatory problems. The intention is to encourage pupils to quickly recall mathematical facts on a short regular basis.

CONTENTS

Oral Maths

Counting on

Pupils sit in a circle and slowly slap the tops of thighs, clap hands then snap fingers – first with one hand then the other. If snapping fingers is difficult then change to wagging a finger on each hand in turn. Continue this to develop a steady rhythm.

■ When the rhythm is steady play 'Follow my number on' where you start with any number. Pupils count on from this number until you say stop.

Thigh	**clap**	**snap**	**snap**	**thigh**	**.... .**
Six	*seven*	*eight*	*nine*	*ten*	*.... .*

If this creates problems then slow down the actions or allow even more thinking time by counting only on the second snap of fingers.

Between the end of one counting sequence and the start of the next there will be a pause but keep the actions and rhythm going continuously whilst giving further instructions.

■ Start counting on from different numbers.
■ Extend to counting on from numbers greater than 20.
■ Tell pupils that they are going to count on by 3. Give them various starting numbers and check that they stop after counting on by 3.
■ Change the counting on number and use different starting points.

Daily Workout Unit 1

Addition bonds to 10

Teaching Tips For Set A

■ Pupils should be confident in answering the addition bonds to 10 and have quick recall for most of the bonds.
■ Timing the exercise can help with encouraging quick recall.

Answers

A
① 5	④ 6	⑦ 8	⑩ 10
② 5	⑤ 8	⑧ 8	⑪ 9
③ 5	⑥ 7	⑨ 10	⑫ 10

B
① 4	④ 10	⑦ 8	⑩ 8
② 9	⑤ 10	⑧ 9	⑪ 9
③ 3	⑥ 7	⑨ 6	⑫ 7

C
① 9	④ 4	⑦ 1	⑩ 2
② 8	⑤ 3	⑧ 0	⑪ 7
③ 6	⑥ 10	⑨ 5	⑫ 11

D ① 5p ② 6p ③ 10p ④ 6p

E ① Square ② Triangle ③ Circle ④ Rectangle

Name	Class	# Unit 1

A

① 4 + 1	....	④ 3 + 3	....	⑦ 4 + 4	....	⑩ 7 + 3	....
② 3 + 2	....	⑤ 1 + 7	....	⑧ 0 + 8	....	⑪ 8 + 1	....
③ 5 + 0	....	⑥ 2 + 5	....	⑨ 5 + 5	....	⑫ 6 + 4	....

B

① 2 + 2	....	④ 1 + 9	....	⑦ 2 + 6	....	⑩ 7 + 1	....
② 4 + 5	....	⑤ 8 + 2	....	⑧ 5 + 4	....	⑪ 8 + 1	....
③ 3 + 0	....	⑥ 3 + 4	....	⑨ 0 + 6	....	⑫ 5 + 2	....

C

Write the numbers.

① Nine	....	④ Four	....	⑦ One	....	⑩ Two	....
② Eight	....	⑤ Three	....	⑧ Zero	....	⑪ Seven	....
③ Six	....	⑥ Ten	....	⑨ Five	....	⑫ Eleven	....

D

Write the total cost.

①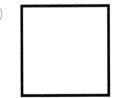

②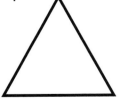

③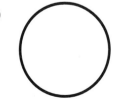

④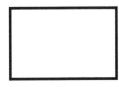

....

E

Write the name of each shape.

① ② ③ ④

....

Oral Maths

Counting back

Pupils sit in a circle and slowly slap the tops of thighs, clap hands then snap fingers – first with one hand then the other. If snapping fingers is difficult then change to wagging a finger on each hand in turn. Continue this to develop a steady rhythm.

■ When the rhythm is steady play 'Follow my number back' where you start with any number. Pupils count back from this number until you say stop.

Thigh	clap	snap	snap	thigh	....
Twelve	*eleven*	*ten*	*nine*	*eight*	*....*

If this creates problems then slow down the actions or allow even more thinking time by counting only on the second snap of fingers.

Between the end of one counting sequence and the start of the next there will be a pause but keep the actions and rhythm going continuously whilst giving further instructions.

■ Start counting back from different numbers.

■ Extend to counting back from numbers greater than 20.

■ Tell pupils that they are going to count back by 3. Give them various starting numbers and check that they stop after counting back by 3.

■ Change the counting back number and use different starting points.

Daily Workout Unit 2

Subtraction bonds within 10

Teaching Tips For Set A

■ Pupils should be confident in answering the subtraction bonds within 10 and have quick recall for most of the bonds.

■ Timing the exercise can help with encouraging quick recall.

Answers

A
① 4	④ 2	⑦ 0	⑩ 4
② 2	⑤ 1	⑧ 9	⑪ 6
③ 3	⑥ 5	⑨ 7	⑫ 4

B
① 4	④ 7	⑦ 8	⑩ 10
② 8	⑤ 4	⑧ 1	⑪ 0
③ 8	⑥ 2	⑨ 7	⑫ 9

C
① 12	④ 15	⑦ 13	⑩ 19
② 17	⑤ 16	⑧ 20	⑪ 11
③ 5	⑥ 8	⑨ 14	⑫ 18

D
① 6p	② 8p	③ 5p	④ 9p

E
① 10	④ 9
② 16	⑤ 15
③ 20	⑥ 19

Name   Class

Unit 2

A

1. 5 – 1 ....
2. 4 – 2 ....
3. 3 – 0 ....
4. 6 – 4 ....
5. 5 – 4 ....
6. 8 – 3 ....
7. 6 – 6 ....
8. 10 – 1 ....
9. 10 – 3 ....
10. 9 – 5 ....
11. 9 – 3 ....
12. 8 – 4 ....

B

1. 3 + 1 ....
2. 4 + 4 ....
3. 5 + 3 ....
4. 2 + 5 ....
5. 7 – 3 ....
6. 6 – 4 ....
7. 8 – 0 ....
8. 5 – 4 ....
9. 10 – 3 ....
10. 6 + 4 ....
11. 5 – 5 ....
12. 7 + 2 ....

C

Write the numbers.

1. Twelve ....
2. Seventeen ....
3. Five ....
4. Fifteen ....
5. Sixteen ....
6. Eight ....
7. Thirteen ....
8. Twenty ....
9. Fourteen ....
10. Nineteen ....
11. Eleven ....
12. Eighteen ....

D

Write the totals.

1. **2**p **2**p **2**p
2. **2**p **1**p **5**p
3. **2**p **2**p **1**p
4. **2**p **2**p **5**p

....

E

Write the missing numbers.

1. 2 4 6 8 ◊ ....
2. 8 10 12 14 ◊ ....
3. 12 14 16 18 ◊ ....
4. 1 3 5 7 ◊ ....
5. 7 9 11 13 ◊ ....
6. 11 13 15 17 ◊ ....

Oral Maths

Quick recall of addition facts to 10

Pupils need to be able to quickly recall the addition facts to 10 and to understand the language associated with addition problems. These activities are intended to check for pupil speed and efficiency.

Each pupil needs a set of Number Cards from the resource sheet on page 62.

| 0 | 1 | 2 | 3 | 4 | 5 | 6 | 7 | 8 | 9 | 10 |

They should hold up one or more of their Number Cards in response to activities such as:

■ quick recall questions where the total is 10 or less
   Show me the answers to: 3 + 3, 2 + 7, 3 + 5, 6 + 4, ...
   Show me two numbers which total: 5, 10, 8, 6, ...

■ quick recall questions where the total is 10
   What must be added to these to make 10? 4, 6, 1, 5, ...
   Show me a pair of numbers which total: 10, another pair, ...

■ questions which use the language of addition, such as:
   Show me 4 plus 6. Show me the total of 3 and 4. What is double 3?
   What is the sum of 3 and 5? Show me 4 more than 2. Increase 2 by 6.

Discuss what happens when you add two odd numbers, two even numbers, one of each. Is the answer odd or even?

Daily Workout Unit 3

Totalling coins to 10p

Teaching Tip For Set A

■ Pupils should be able to add quickly 1p, 2p and 5p coins within a total of 10p.

Answers

A ① 3p   ④ 6p
   ② 7p   ⑤ 10p
   ③ 4p   ⑥ 6p

B ① 8   ④ 3   ⑦ 8   ⑩ 1
   ② 3   ⑤ 8   ⑧ 7   ⑪ 9
   ③ 8   ⑥ 0   ⑨ 10   ⑫ 3

C ① 7   ⑤ 7
   ② 7   ⑥ 2
   ③ 7   ⑦ 8
   ④ 7   ⑧ 2

D ① 5p   ③ 3p   **E** ① 0   ④ 1
   ② 8p   ④ 10p   ② 4   ⑤ 7
                           ③ 10   ⑥ 11

Name .... Class ....

A

① (**2**p) + (**1**p) ....   ④ (**1**p) + (**5**p) ....

② (**5**p) + (**2**p) ....   ⑤ (**5**p) + (**5**p) ....

③ (**2**p) + (**2**p) ....   ⑥ (**2**p) + (**2**p) + (**2**p) ....

B

① 3 + 5 ....   ④ 9 − 6 ....   ⑦ 5 + 3 ....   ⑩ 10 − 9 ....

② 10 − 7 ....   ⑤ 6 + 2 ....   ⑧ 7 − 0 ....   ⑪ 3 + 6 ....

③ 4 + 4 ....   ⑥ 6 − 6 ....   ⑨ 2 + 8 ....   ⑫ 8 − 5 ....

C

① 2 more than 5 ....   ⑤ 1 less than 8 ....

② 3 more than 4 ....   ⑥ 3 less than 5 ....

③ 1 more than 6 ....   ⑦ 2 less than 10 ....

④ 4 more than 3 ....   ⑧ 4 less than 6 ....

D

① How much is in purse A? ....

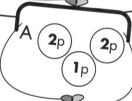

③ How much more in purse B than purse A? ....

② How much is in purse B? ....

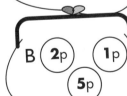

④ How much in purse A if 5p more is put in? ....

E

Write the missing numbers.

① 8 6 4 2 ◊ ....   ④ 9 7 5 3 ◊ ....

② 12 10 8 6 ◊ ....   ⑤ 15 13 11 9 ◊ ....

③ 18 16 14 12 ◊ ....   ⑥ 19 17 15 13 ◊ ....

Mental Maths *Daily Workout* **Book 1**

Oral Maths

Quick recall of subtraction facts within 10

Pupils need to be able to quickly recall the subtraction facts to 10 and to understand the language associated with subtraction problems. These activities are intended to check for pupil speed and efficiency.

Each pupil needs a set of Number Cards from the resource sheet on page 62

They should hold up one or more of their Number Cards in response to activities such as:

- quick recall questions such as:
    Show me the answers to: 9 – 7, 4 – 2, 6 – 0, 10 – 4, ...
    Show me two numbers which have a difference of: 1, 3, 2, 4, ...

- quick recall questions such as:
    Show me two numbers which have a difference of: 2, another two numbers, ...

- questions which use the language of subtraction:
    Show me 10 minus 6. Show me 5 subtract 2. What is 4 less than 7?
    What is the difference between 5 and 7? Take away 4 from 10.
    Decrease 8 by 6. Subtract 2 from 6.

Discuss what happens when you subtract two odd numbers, two even numbers, one of each. Is the answer odd or even?

Daily Workout Unit 4

Pairs which total 10

Teaching Tips For Set A

- Check that pupils can quickly recall all number pairs which total 10.
- Quick recognition of pairs which total 10 is an important mental skill for pupils to acquire.

Answers

A ① 6 ④ 8 ⑦ 5
  ② 7 ⑤ 2 ⑧ 3
  ③ 4 ⑥ 9 ⑨ 1

B ① 6p ④ 8p ⑦ 5p ⑩ 10p
  ② 7p ⑤ 10p ⑧ 9p ⑪ 9p
  ③ 4p ⑥ 10p ⑨ 10p ⑫ 7p

C ① 7 ⑤ 4
  ② 7 ⑥ 4
  ③ 9 ⑦ 8
  ④ 8 ⑧ 2

D ① 6 stamps ③ 2 stamps
  ② 8 stamps ④ 8 stamps

E ① Tuesday ④ Friday
  ② Saturday ⑤ Wednesday
  ③ Thursday ⑥ Sunday

Name	Class	# Unit 4

A

Each pair must add up to 10.
Write the missing number.

① 4, ◊ ....   ④ ◊, 2 ....   ⑦ 5, ◊ ....

② 3, ◊ ....   ⑤ ◊, 8 ....   ⑧ 7, ◊ ....

③ 6, ◊ ....   ⑥ ◊, 1 ....   ⑨ 9, ◊ ....

B

① 4p + 2p ....   ④ 3p + 5p ....   ⑦ 3p + 2p ....   ⑩ 4p + 6p ....

② 6p + 1p ....   ⑤ 9p + 1p ....   ⑧ 7p + 2p ....   ⑪ 2p + 7p ....

③ 2p + 2p ....   ⑥ 5p + 5p ....   ⑨ 6p + 4p ....   ⑫ 3p + 4p ....

C

① Add 2 to 5 ....   ⑤ Subtract 3 from 7 ....

② Add 3 and 4 ....   ⑥ Subtract 4 from 8 ....

③ 4 add 5 ....   ⑦ 10 subtract 2 ....

④ 6 add on 2 ....   ⑧ 7 subtract 5 ....

D

① Martin has four stamps.
Lita has two stamps.
How many stamps altogether? ....

② Paul has six stamps.
Emma has two more stamps than him.
How many stamps has Emma? ....

③ Jo has six stamps.
She loses four stamps.
How many are left? ....

④ Simon has three stamps.
He buys five more.
How many has he now? ....

E

Write which day follows these.

① Monday ....   ④ Thursday ....

② Friday ....   ⑤ Tuesday ....

③ Wednesday ....   ⑥ Saturday ....

Oral Maths

Addition and subtraction trios

Pupils should know the addition and subtraction trios to 10 and the relationships between such numbers, especially inverses, such as addition being the 'opposite' of subtraction.

The trios for 10 to 7 are as follows:

10...	10,0	9...	9,0	8...	8,0	7...	7,0
	9,1		8,1		7,1		6,1
	8,2		7,2		6,2		5,2
	7,3		6,3		5,3		4,3
	6,4		5,4		4,4		
	5,5						

The other trios follow on in the same way.

Taking an addition and subtraction trio such as 9, 7, 2 as an example, pupils should be able to state many possible number sentences which use these three numbers. For example:

> 7 plus 2 equals 9.   9 take away 7 leaves 2.   7 is 2 less than 9.
> 9 minus 7 equals 2.   The difference between 9 and 2 is 7.
> 2 more than 7 is 9.   The sum of 2 and 7 is 9.   9 subtract 7 equals 2.

■ Give pupils an addition and subtraction trio such as 10, 6, 4 and ask each one in turn to give a different number sentence which uses these three numbers. Encourage them to listen carefully to what has been said so as not to repeat a sentence. The sentences can be recorded on the board, or on a chart.

■ Focus on the inverse by asking questions such as:
> If 3 + 4 = 7, what is 7 – 4? If 7 – 3 = 4, what is 4 + 3?

Daily Workout Unit 5

Totalling three numbers

Teaching Tips For Set A

■ Many schemes only give practice in the addition of number pairs and need supplementing.

■ Discuss the fact that the number can be added in any order. Question whether it may be quicker to add in a certain order.

Answers

A
① 7	④ 6	⑦ 9	⑩ 9
② 8	⑤ 8	⑧ 8	⑪ 9
③ 10	⑥ 8	⑨ 6	⑫ 10

B
① 10	④ 10	⑦ 8	⑩ 7
② 7	⑤ 10	⑧ 9	⑪ 0
③ 0	⑥ 8	⑨ 9	⑫ 5

C
① 7	④ 6	⑦ 3	⑩ 2
② 7	⑤ 7	⑧ 6	⑪ 4
③ 10	⑥ 2	⑨ 8	⑫ 10

D   ① 5p   ② 7p   ③ 9p   ④ 8p

E   ① Square   ② Hexagon   ③ Oval   ④ Triangle

A

1. 1 + 2 + 4 ....
2. 3 + 2 + 3 ....
3. 4 + 4 + 2 ....
4. 2 + 3 + 1 ....
5. 5 + 1 + 2 ....
6. 4 + 2 + 2 ....
7. 3 + 3 + 3 ....
8. 2 + 1 + 5 ....
9. 2 + 2 + 2 ....
10. 3 + 1 + 5 ....
11. 2 + 2 + 5 ....
12. 5 + 3 + 2 ....

B

1. 5 + 5 ....
2. 10 − 3 ....
3. 6 − 6 ....
4. 8 + 2 ....
5. 7 + 3 ....
6. 10 − 2 ....
7. 5 + 3 ....
8. 7 + 2 ....
9. 8 + 1 ....
10. 0 + 7 ....
11. 9 − 9 ....
12. 5 − 0 ....

C

1. 3 plus 4 ....
2. 5 plus 2 ....
3. 6 plus 4 ....
4. 3 plus 3 ....
5. 8 minus 1 ....
6. 6 minus 4 ....
7. 5 minus 2 ....
8. 10 minus 4 ....
9. 4 plus 4 ....
10. 5 minus 3 ....
11. 10 minus 6 ....
12. 3 plus 7 ....

D

1. Lee has 10p.
   He spends 5p
   How much has he left? ....

2. Nadine has 4p.
   She finds 3p.
   How much has she now? ....

3. Lisa has 6p.
   Fran has 3p more.
   How much has Fran? ....

4. Simone has 10p.
   Ben has 2p less.
   How much has Ben? ....

E

Write the name of each shape.

1.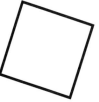
2.
3.
4.

....

Mental Maths *Daily Workout* **Book 1**

Oral Maths

Quick recall of number facts to 10

Pupils sit in groups of between five and ten.

Each group makes a set of Cycle Cards so that each pupil has at least one card. Cycle Cards have a sum on one side and the answer to a different Cycle Card sum on the reverse. Each answer should be a different number.

The sums should include addition and subtraction facts to 10. Pupils can include the addition of more than two numbers in their sums, such as 2 + 3 + 4.

- One child begins by reading the sum on his or her Cycle Card.
- The person who has the answer says *I have the answer which is ...*
- Then that person reads out the sum on the reverse for another pupil to answer.
- This continues until all the sums have been answered.
- The cards are then swapped around amongst the group and the activity repeated.

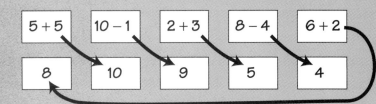

Daily Workout Unit 6

Inverse of addition

Teaching Tips For Set A

- Pupils need to know that addition and subtraction are inverses.
- They should realise that although a function machine may show an addition, to calculate the input a subtraction will be necessary.

Answers

A
- ① 1
- ② 2
- ③ 0
- ④ 3
- ⑤ 5
- ⑥ 7
- ⑦ 4
- ⑧ 8
- ⑨ 6

B
- ① 10
- ② 7
- ③ 10
- ④ 1
- ⑤ 3
- ⑥ 8
- ⑦ 7
- ⑧ 0
- ⑨ 8
- ⑩ 10
- ⑪ 8
- ⑫ 8

C
- ① 6
- ② 9
- ③ 3
- ④ 4
- ⑤ 10
- ⑥ 3
- ⑦ 9
- ⑧ 6

E
- ① Four
- ② Ten
- ③ Six
- ④ Eight
- ⑤ Five
- ⑥ Nine
- ⑦ Eleven
- ⑧ Seven
- ⑨ Twelve

D
- ① 7
- ② 6
- ③ 8
- ④ 6

A

These numbers have been through the machine.
Write which numbers went in.

In   + 2   Out

① 3   ....   ④ 5   ....   ⑦ 6   ....

② 4   ....   ⑤ 7   ....   ⑧ 10   ....

③ 2   ....   ⑥ 9   ....   ⑨ 8   ....

B

① $4 + 6$ ....   ④ $9 - 8$ ....   ⑦ $7 - 0$ ....   ⑩ $2 + 2 + 6$ ....

② $10 - 3$ ....   ⑤ $8 - 5$ ....   ⑧ $5 - 5$ ....   ⑪ $5 + 1 + 2$ ....

③ $5 + 5$ ....   ⑥ $4 + 4$ ....   ⑨ $4 + 3 + 1$ ....   ⑫ $3 + 3 + 2$ ....

C

① 4 more than 2   ....   ⑤ Add 3 to 7   ....

② 3 more than 6   ....   ⑥ Subtract 4 from 7   ....

③ 2 less than 5   ....   ⑦ 5 plus 4   ....

④ 5 less than 9   ....   ⑧ 8 minus 2   ....

D

① Which number is 3 more than 4?   ....

② Which number is 4 less than 10?   ....

③ What is the total of 5 and 3?   ....

④ What is 5 plus 2 minus 1?   ....

E

Write these in words.

① 4 ....   ④ 8 ....   ⑦ 11 ....

② 10 ....   ⑤ 5 ....   ⑧ 7 ....

③ 6 ....   ⑥ 9 ....   ⑨ 12 ....

Oral Maths

Telling the time – o'clock and half past

Each pupil needs a Clock Face. They can use the one from the resource sheet on page 64.

- Ask pupils to show stated o'clock times on their clock faces.
  Show me: 3 o'clock, 6 o'clock, 11 o'clock, noon, ...

- Continue to include half past the hour.
  Show me: half past 6, half past 9 , half past 3, ...

- Extend to using the hour before and the hour later.
  Show me one hour before: 3 o'clock, 6 o'clock, 4 o'clock, ...
  Show me one hour after: 10 o'clock, 2 o'clock, 7 o'clock, ...
  Show me one hour after: half past 8, half past 3, half past 10, ...
  Show me one hour before: half past 3, half past 11, half past 2, ...

- Decide whether to include quarter past and quarter to in the activities.

Daily Workout Unit 7

Solving equations of the type 3 + ◊ = 8

Teaching Tips For Set A

- Discuss techniques for solving equations such as 3 + ◊ = 8. These include:
  ~ counting on
  ~ using the inverse of addition and subtracting 3 from 8
  ~ using quick recall of the number bond.

- It can help to put the problem into words such as:
  Three plus a number equals eight.
  What is the number?

Answers

A
- ① 5
- ② 3
- ③ 9
- ④ 3
- ⑤ 5
- ⑥ 1
- ⑦ 0
- ⑧ 1
- ⑨ 3
- ⑩ 4
- ⑪ 4
- ⑫ 3

B
- ① 6p
- ② 6p
- ③ 9p
- ④ 8p
- ⑤ 3p
- ⑥ 6p
- ⑦ 7p
- ⑧ 8p
- ⑨ 10p
- ⑩ 9p
- ⑪ 10p
- ⑫ 4p

C
- ① 20
- ② 70
- ③ 50
- ④ 60
- ⑤ 30
- ⑥ 100
- ⑦ 40
- ⑧ 80
- ⑨ 90

E
- ① Saturday
- ② Thursday
- ③ Tuesday
- ④ Monday
- ⑤ Wednesday
- ⑥ Sunday

D
- ① 5p
- ② 2p
- ③ 7p
- ④ 6p

Unit 7

A

Write the missing numbers.

1. $3 + \diamond = 8$ ....
2. $4 + \diamond = 7$ ....
3. $1 + \diamond = 10$ ....
4. $2 + \diamond = 5$ ....
5. $5 + \diamond = 10$ ....
6. $8 + \diamond = 9$ ....
7. $6 + \diamond = 6$ ....
8. $3 + \diamond = 4$ ....
9. $7 + \diamond = 10$ ....
10. $2 + \diamond = 6$ ....
11. $4 + \diamond = 8$ ....
12. $6 + \diamond = 9$ ....

B

1. $4p + 2p$ ....
2. $5p + 1p$ ....
3. $3p + 6p$ ....
4. $4p + 4p$ ....
5. $10p - 7p$ ....
6. $10p - 4p$ ....
7. $10p - 3p$ ....
8. $10p - 2p$ ....
9. $5p + 5p$ ....
10. $10p - 1p$ ....
11. $2p + 8p$ ....
12. $10p - 6p$ ....

C

Write these using numbers.

1. Twenty ....
2. Seventy ....
3. Fifty ....
4. Sixty ....
5. Thirty ....
6. One hundred ....
7. Forty ....
8. Eighty ....
9. Ninety ....

D

1. What is the total cost of stamps A and B? ....
2. How much more is stamp C than stamp A? ....
3. What is the cost of stamps B and C? ....
4. What would two stamp B's cost? ....

A **2**p

B **3**p

C **4**p

E

Write which day comes before these.

1. Sunday ....
2. Friday ....
3. Wednesday ....
4. Tuesday ....
5. Thursday ....
6. Monday ....

Oral Maths

Counting in tens

Pupils sit in a circle and slowly slap the tops of thighs, clap hands then snap fingers – first with one hand then the other. If snapping fingers is difficult then change to wagging a finger on each hand in turn. Continue this to develop a steady rhythm.

■ When the rhythm is steady play 'Count in tens' starting with any decade number. Pupils count on from this number until they reach 100. This limit can be removed if appropriate.

Thigh	**clap**	**snap**	**snap**	**thigh**	**... .**
Thirty	*forty*	*fifty*	*sixty*	*seventy*	*... .*

■ Start counting on from different decade numbers.

■ Extend to counting back in tens from different decade numbers.

Each pupil needs a strip of scrap card, approximately 30 cm long and 5 cm wide, which has been divided into 10 parts.

Wind an elastic band around each strip. The elastic band should be sufficiently tight on the strip so that it does not slip up and down.

■ Tell pupils that one end of the strip is zero and the other end is one hundred. Ask them to slide the elastic band along to show the position of 70 on the strip. They should hold up their strips to show their results. Repeat for different decade numbers between 0 and 100.

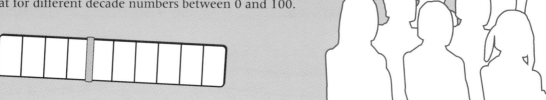

Daily Workout Unit 8

Solving equations of the type ◊ + 1 = 8

Teaching Tips For Set A

■ Discuss techniques for solving equations such as ◊ + 1 = 8
These include:
~ knowing about commutativity and counting on
~ using inverse of addition and subtracting 1 from 8
~ using quick recall of the number bond.

■ It can help to put the problem into words. For example:
A number plus one equals eight.
What is the number?

Answers

A
① 7	④ 6	⑦ 7	⑩ 2
② 1	⑤ 4	⑧ 3	⑪ 0
③ 0	⑥ 2	⑨ 3	⑫ 8

B
① 9	④ 10	⑦ 0	⑩ 1
② 5	⑤ 10	⑧ 5	⑪ 7
③ 1	⑥ 2	⑨ 2	⑫ 8

C ① 6   ② 6   ③ 6   ④ 4   ⑤ 6

D ① Fran   ② Susheela   ③ Colin   ④ John   ⑤ John

E ① 5p   ② 2p   ③ 2p

Name .... Class ....

A Write the missing numbers.

① ◊ + 1 = 8 .... ④ ◊ + 4 = 10 .... ⑦ ◊ + 2 = 9 .... ⑩ ◊ + 2 = 4 ....

② ◊ + 9 = 10 .... ⑤ ◊ + 3 = 7 .... ⑧ ◊ + 7 = 10 .... ⑪ ◊ + 8 = 8 ....

③ ◊ + 5 = 5 .... ⑥ ◊ + 6 = 8 .... ⑨ ◊ + 3 = 6 .... ⑫ ◊ +1 = 9 ....

B Write the missing numbers.

① 5 + 4 = ◊ .... ④ 9 + 1 = ◊ .... ⑦ ◊ + 5 = 5 .... ⑩ ◊ + 5 = 6 ....

② ◊ + 5 = 10 .... ⑤ 8 + 2 = ◊ .... ⑧ 4 + ◊ = 9 .... ⑪ ◊ + 3 = 10 ....

③ 7 + ◊ = 8 .... ⑥ ◊ + 3 = 5 .... ⑨ 6 + ◊ = 8 .... ⑫ 4 + 4 = ◊ ....

C

① The difference between 2 and 8 is ....

② The difference between 9 and 3 is ....

③ The difference between 6 and 0 is ....

④ The difference between 5 and 9 is ....

⑤ The difference between 1 and 7 is ....

D

Name	Score
John	3
Fran	5
Susheela	2
Colin	4

① Who scored the most points? ....

② Who scored the fewest points? ....

③ Who scored two more than Susheela? ....

④ Who scored two fewer than Fran? ....

⑤ Who scored one more than Susheela? ....

E

Each purse should have 10p.
Write the missing coin.

①

②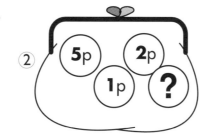

③

....

Oral Maths

Talking about TU numbers

Pupils should sit in a circle and give different facts about a stated number, such as 36.

Encourage a wide range of different types of fact. For example:

Tell me about 36.

- **place value and position**
  36 is made up of 30 and 6.
  36 is 3 tens and 6 units.
  36 is between 35 and 37.

- **simple addition and subtraction facts**
  36 is 35 + 1.
  36 is 37 − 1.
  36 is 20 and 10 and 6.

- **number facts**
  36 is an even number.
  36 is not an odd number.
  36 is greater than 20.

Pupils should try not to repeat a fact which has been used previously.
They should learn to adapt what someone else has said.

Daily Workout Unit 9

Inverse of subtraction

Teaching Tips For Set A

- Pupils need to know that subtraction and addition are inverses.
- They should realise that although a function machine may show a subtraction, to calculate the input an addition will be necessary.

Answers

A
① 3	④ 5	⑦ 6
② 4	⑤ 7	⑧ 10
③ 1	⑥ 9	⑨ 8

B
① 10	④ 10	⑦ 0	⑩ 10
② 6	⑤ 7	⑧ 4	⑪ 10
③ 7	⑥ 3	⑨ 8	⑫ 10

C ① 10   ② 10   ③ 7   ④ 10   ⑤ 11

D ① 3p   ② 8p   ③ 4p   ④ 2p

E ① Hexagon   ② Rectangle   ③ Diamond   ④ Square
or Rhombus

Name .... Class ....

A

These numbers have been through the machine.
Write which numbers went in.

In — 1 Out

① 2 ....   ④ 4 ....   ⑦ 5 ....
② 3 ....   ⑤ 6 ....   ⑧ 9 ....
③ 0 ....   ⑥ 8 ....   ⑨ 7 ....

B

① 4 + 6 ....   ④ 5 + 5 ....   ⑦ 7 − 7 ....   ⑩ 8 + 1 + 1 ....
② 6 + 0 ....   ⑤ 10 − 3 ....   ⑧ 7 − 3 ....   ⑪ 3 + 3 + 4 ....
③ 5 + 2 ....   ⑥ 9 − 6 ....   ⑨ 4 + 1 + 3 ....   ⑫ 2 + 3 + 5 ....

C

① The total of 4 and 6 is ....
② The total of 8 and 2 is ....
③ The total of 1, 2 and 4 is ....
④ The total of 2, 3 and 5 is ....
⑤ The total of 2, 3 and 6 is ....

D

① Lisa has 8p.
She spends 5p.
How much is left? ....

② Tom paid with 10p.
His change was 2p.
How much did he spend? ....

③ Sam had 2p.
His sister had twice as much.
How much had his sister? ....

④ Gita had 4p.
Her sister had half as much.
How much had her sister? ....

E

Write the name of each shape.

①    ②    ③    ④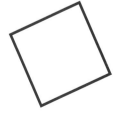

....

Oral Maths

Counting on

Pupils should be able to use counting on skills in two different situations:

- from any two digit number by a small number
- from one number to another close number.

Decide whether fingers can be used to keep a record of the count.

Ask questions such as:

> *What is 2 more than 23? What is 1 more than 26? What is 3 more than 35?*
> *Add 2 to these numbers: 17, 23, 28, 34, 42, ...*

Pupils can find the differences between two close numbers by counting on.

> *What is the difference between: 13 and 16, 17 and 19, 24 and 26, ... ?*
> *How many jumps are there between these numbers: 15 and 18, 21 and 24, 26 and 29, ... ?*

Pupils can write their answers on small pieces of scrap paper and hold these up when instructed to do so. This overcomes the problem of answers being called out.

Daily Workout Unit 10

Solving equations of the type 7 – ◊ = 2

Teaching Tips For Set A

- Discuss possible techniques for solving equations such as 7 – ◊ = 2. These include:
    - ~ counting back to the answer
    - ~ using quick recall of the number bond.
- It can help to put the problem into words such as:
    Seven subtract a number leaves two.
    What is the number?

Answers

A
① 5	④ 3	⑦ 3	⑩ 1
② 3	⑤ 8	⑧ 0	⑪ 3
③ 5	⑥ 5	⑨ 9	⑫ 7

B
① 7	⑤ 2
② 9	⑥ 0
③ 8	⑦ 5
④ 8	⑧ 2

C   ① 9   ② 7   ③ 10   ④ 9   ⑤ 6

D   ① Fiona   ② Marie   ③ Fiona   ④ David   ⑤ Five years

E   ① 3 o'clock   ② 6 o'clock   ③ 10 o'clock   ④ 2 o'clock

Unit 10

A

Write the missing numbers.

1. $7 - \Diamond = 2$ ....
2. $4 - \Diamond = 1$ ....
3. $10 - \Diamond = 5$ ....

4. $9 - \Diamond = 6$ ....
5. $10 - \Diamond = 2$ ....
6. $8 - \Diamond = 3$ ....

7. $3 - \Diamond = 0$ ....
8. $7 - \Diamond = 7$ ....
9. $10 - \Diamond = 1$ ....

10. $5 - \Diamond = 4$ ....
11. $6 - \Diamond = 3$ ....
12. $10 - \Diamond = 3$ ....

B

1. $4 + 2 + 1$ ....
2. $5 + 1 + 3$ ....
3. $6 + 0 + 2$ ....
4. $2 + 2 + 4$ ....

5. $5 - 2 - 1$ ....
6. $6 - 3 - 3$ ....
7. $8 - 2 - 1$ ....
8. $7 - 3 - 2$ ....

C

1. The sum of 8 and 1 is ....
2. The sum of 2 and 5 is ....
3. The sum of 2, 3 and 5 is ....
4. The sum of 1, 5 and 3 is ....
5. The sum of 2, 2 and 2 is ....

D

1. Who is the oldest? ....
2. Who is the youngest? ....
3. Who is twice as old as David? ....
4. Who is half as old as Fiona? ....
5. How much older is Fiona than Marie? ....

Marie 3 today!

David 4 today!

Fiona 8 today!

E

Write the times.

1.
2.
3.
4.

....

Oral Maths

Counting back

Pupils should be able to use counting back skills in two different situations:

■ from any two digit number by a small number

■ from one number to another close number.

Decide whether fingers can be used to keep a record of the count.

Ask questions such as:

What is 2 less than 23? What is 1 less than 26? What is 3 less than 35?
Subtract 2 from these numbers: 17, 23, 28, 34, 42, ...

Pupils can find the differences between two close numbers by counting back.

What is the difference between: 15 and 12, 17 and 13, 28 and 26, ... ?
How many jumps are there between these numbers: 15 and 11, 19 and 17, 26 and 21, ... ?

Pupils can write their answers on small pieces of scrap paper and hold these up when instructed to do so. This overcomes the problem of answers being called out.

Daily Workout Unit 11

Solving equations of the type ◊ − 2 = 5

Teaching Tips For Set A

■ Equations such as ◊ − 2 = 5 often cause errors. Discuss possible techniques for solving these types of equations such as:

~ using inverses and adding 2 and 5
~ using quick recall of the number bond.

■ It can help to put the problem into words such as:

A number subtract two leaves five.
What is the number?

Answers

A
- ① 7
- ② 9
- ③ 4
- ④ 8
- ⑤ 8
- ⑥ 9
- ⑦ 10
- ⑧ 10
- ⑨ 7
- ⑩ 10
- ⑪ 9
- ⑫ 10

B
- ① 7
- ② 5
- ③ 0
- ④ 2
- ⑤ 6
- ⑥ 9
- ⑦ 3
- ⑧ 6
- ⑨ 7
- ⑩ 0
- ⑪ 10
- ⑫ 8

C
- ① 8
- ② 8
- ③ 10
- ④ 8
- ⑤ 2
- ⑥ 9
- ⑦ 6
- ⑧ 9

D
- ① B
- ② A
- ③ A
- ④ C

E
- ① Twelve
- ② Fifteen
- ③ Twenty
- ④ Eleven
- ⑤ Thirteen
- ⑥ Eighteen
- ⑦ Seventeen
- ⑧ Sixteen
- ⑨ Nineteen

A

Write the missing numbers.

① ◊ − 2 = 5   ....   ④ ◊ − 2 = 6   ....   ⑦ ◊ − 9 = 1   ....   ⑩ ◊ − 2 = 8   ....

② ◊ − 3 = 6   ....   ⑤ ◊ − 5 = 3   ....   ⑧ ◊ − 3 = 7   ....   ⑪ ◊ − 4 = 5   ....

③ ◊ − 4 = 0   ....   ⑥ ◊ − 2 = 7   ....   ⑨ ◊ − 5 = 2   ....   ⑫ ◊ − 6 = 4   ....

B

Write the missing numbers.

① 10 − 3 = ◊   ....   ④ 4 − ◊ = 2   ....   ⑦ 7 − 4 = ◊   ....   ⑩ 7 − ◊ = 7   ....

② 7 − 2 = ◊   ....   ⑤ ◊ − 3 = 3   ....   ⑧ 6 − ◊ = 0   ....   ⑪ ◊ − 1 = 9   ....

③ 5 − ◊ = 5   ....   ⑥ ◊ − 5 = 4   ....   ⑨ 9 − ◊ = 2   ....   ⑫ ◊ − 3 = 5   ....

C

① Add together 5 and 3   ....   ⑤ Four less than 6   ....

② Subtract 2 from 10   ....   ⑥ The sum of 6 and 3   ....

③ Total 3 and 7   ....   ⑦ The difference between 2 and 8   ....

④ Two more than 6   ....   ⑧ The total of 2, 4 and 3   ....

D

Which shape is cut in half?

① ....

② ....

③ ....

④ ....

E

Write these numbers in words.

① 12 ....   ④ 11 ....   ⑦ 17 ....

② 15 ....   ⑤ 13 ....   ⑧ 16 ....

③ 20 ....   ⑥ 18 ....   ⑨ 19 ....

Oral Maths

0	1	2	3	4	5	6	7	8	9	10
11	12	13	14	15	16	17	18	19	20	

Addition facts to 20

Pupils need to be confident with the addition facts to 20 and to understand the language associated with addition problems.

Each pupil needs a set of Number Cards from the resource sheet on page 62.

They should hold up one or more of their Number Cards in response to activities such as:

■ quick recall questions where the numbers being added are single digit numbers
Show me the answers to: 8 + 8, 9 + 4, 6 + 5, 4 + 7, ...
Show me two single numbers which total: 11, 14, 12, 15, ...

■ quick recall questions where the numbers being added include a teen number
Show me the answers to: 12 + 2, 2 + 13, 15 + 4, 3 + 14, ...
Show me a teen number and a single number which total: 16, 18, 20, 14, ...

■ questions which use the language of addition
Show me 4 plus 7. Show me the total of 9 and 4. What is double 7?
What is the sum of 6 and 5? Show me 4 more than 9. Increase 9 by 6.

Discuss what happens when you add two odd numbers, two even numbers, one of each. Is the answer odd or even?

Daily Workout Unit 12

Mixed addition and subtraction

Teaching Tips For Set A

■ Pupils should be confident in solving simple chain sums which include a mix of addition and subtraction operations.

■ Check that they are mainly using quick recall of number facts when solving the sums.

■ Discuss whether the order of doing the addition and subtraction makes a difference to the answer.

Answers

A
1. 7
2. 4
3. 3
4. 2
5. 7
6. 9
7. 10
8. 7
9. 8
10. 9
11. 4
12. 8

B
1. 9
2. 5
3. 9
4. 8
5. 8
6. 8
7. 8
8. 10
9. 9
10. 8
11. 6
12. 10

C
1. 7
2. 10
3. 6
4. 6
5. 5
6. 4
7. 2
8. 10

D
1. 5p
2. 8p
3. 5
4. 8p
5. 6p

E
1. 6
2. 3
3. 2
4. 8
5. 9
6. 0
7. 5
8. 7
9. 4

A

① $4 + 6 - 3$ ....   ④ $6 + 1 - 5$ ....   ⑦ $6 - 3 + 7$ ....   ⑩ $6 - 2 + 5$ ....

② $3 + 2 - 1$ ....   ⑤ $8 - 2 + 1$ ....   ⑧ $5 - 4 + 6$ ....   ⑪ $2 + 6 - 4$ ....

③ $5 + 2 - 4$ ....   ⑥ $5 - 1 + 5$ ....   ⑨ $5 + 5 - 2$ ....   ⑫ $5 - 3 + 6$ ....

B

Total each pair of numbers.

① 5,4 ....   ④ 8,0 ....   ⑦ 3,5 ....   ⑩ 2,6 ....

② 3,2 ....   ⑤ 1,7 ....   ⑧ 0,10 ....   ⑪ 3,3 ....

③ 6,3 ....   ⑥ 4,4 ....   ⑨ 4,5 ....   ⑫ 7,3 ....

C

① 10 is 3 more than ....   ⑤ 10 is 5 more than ....

② 6 is 4 less than ....   ⑥ 2 is 2 less than ....

③ 8 is 2 more than ....   ⑦ 5 is 3 more than ....

④ 5 is 1 less than ....   ⑧ 7 is 3 less than ....

D

① What is half of 10p? ....

② What is twice as much as 4p? ....

③ How many 2p coins make 10p ....

④ What is the total of four 2p coins? ....

⑤ What is the total of two 2p coins and two 1p coins? ....

E

Each pair must total 10.
Write the missing number.

① 4, ◇ ....   ④ 2, ◇ ....   ⑦ 5, ◇ ....

② ◇, 7 ....   ⑤ 1, ◇ ....   ⑧ 3, ◇ ....

③ ◇, 8 ....   ⑥ 10, ◇ ....   ⑨ ◇, 6 ....

Oral Maths

Subtraction facts to 20

Pupils need to be confident with the subtraction facts to 20 and to understand the language associated with subtraction problems.

Each pupil needs a set of Number Cards from the resource sheet on page 62.

They should hold up one or more of their Number Cards in response to activities such as:

■ questions where the numbers being subtracted result in single digit answers

Show me the answers to: 11 – 7, 13 – 6, 14 – 7, 11 – 4, … .
Show me two numbers which have a difference of: 1, 4, 3, 2, … .

■ questions where the answers include a teen number

Show me the answers to: 20 – 5, 16 – 2, 17 – 1, 18 – 3, … .
Show me two numbers which have a difference of: 12, 11, 15, 14, … .

■ questions which use the language of subtraction

Show me 14 minus 8. Show me 12 subtract 6. What is 4 less than 11?
What is the difference between 15 and 10? Take away 4 from 16.
Decrease 18 by 6.

Discuss what happens when you subtract two odd numbers, two even numbers, one of each. Is the answer odd or even?

Daily Workout Unit 13

Adding 10 to digits

Teaching Tips For Set A

■ Pupils should be able to add 10 to a digit to create a teen number.

■ Discuss commutativity so that they realise that, for instance, 7 + 10 = 10 + 7.

Answers

A
- ① 14
- ② 17
- ③ 15
- ④ 16
- ⑤ 13
- ⑥ 19
- ⑦ 11
- ⑧ 18
- ⑨ 12
- ⑩ 14
- ⑪ 16
- ⑫ 19

B
- ① 10
- ② 8
- ③ 10
- ④ 8
- ⑤ 7
- ⑥ 3
- ⑦ 3
- ⑧ 0
- ⑨ 4
- ⑩ 8
- ⑪ 6
- ⑫ 10

C
- ① 9
- ② 5
- ③ 2
- ④ 5
- ⑤ 6
- ⑥ 10
- ⑦ 1
- ⑧ 0

D
- ① 4p
- ② 9p
- ③ 7p
- ④ 5p

E
- ① 10 o'clock
- ② 11 o'clock
- ③ 3 o'clock
- ④ 7 o'clock

A

① 10 + 4 ....   ④ 6 + 10 ....   ⑦ 1 + 10 ....   ⑩ 4 + 10 ....

② 7 + 10 ....   ⑤ 10 + 3 ....   ⑧ 8 + 10 ....   ⑪ 10 + 6 ....

③ 10 + 5 ....   ⑥ 10 + 9 ....   ⑨ 10 + 2 ....   ⑫ 9 + 10 ....

B

① 5 + 4 + 1 ....   ④ 2 + 2 + 4 ....   ⑦ 10 − 5 − 2 ....   ⑩ 6 − 2 + 4 ....

② 3 + 2 + 3 ....   ⑤ 10 − 2 − 1 ....   ⑧ 8 − 6 − 2 ....   ⑪ 5 + 5 − 4 ....

③ 4 + 0 + 6 ....   ⑥ 9 − 3 − 3 ....   ⑨ 2 + 5 − 3 ....   ⑫ 8 − 1 + 3 ....

C

① Add 4 to 5   ....   ⑤ 10 minus 4   ....

② Take 2 from 7   ....   ⑥ 8 plus 2   ....

③ Subtract 4 from 6   ....   ⑦ 7 subtract 6   ....

④ Total 2 and 3   ....   ⑧ 5 take away 5   ....

D

① You have ⑤p, ②p, ①p. You spend ▨4p▨ . How much is left?   ....

② You have ②p, ②p. You find ⑤p. How much have you?   ....

③ You have ⑤p, ②p, ②p. You lose ②p. How much have you?   ....

④ You have ②p, ②p, ①p. You need ⑩p. How much more do you need?   ....

E

Write the times.

① 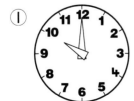   ②    ③ 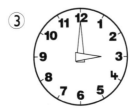   ④

....

Oral Maths

Addition and subtraction trios

Pupils should begin to know the addition and subtraction trios to 20 and the relationships between such numbers, especially inverses, such as addition being the 'opposite' of subtraction.

The trios for 10 to 13 are as follows:

	10...	10,0	11...	10,1	12...	10,2	13...	10,3
		9,1		9,2		9,3		9,4
		8,2		8,3		8,4		8,5
		7,3		7,4		7,5		7,6
		6,4		6,5		6,6		
		5,5						

The other trios follow on in the same way.

Taking an addition and subtraction trio such as 12, 8, 4 as an example, pupils should be able to state many possible number sentences which use these three numbers. For example:

8 plus 4 equals 12. *12 take away 8 leaves 4.* *4 is 8 less than 12.*
12 minus 8 equals 4. *The difference between 12 and 4 is 8.*
4 more than 8 is 12.

■ Give pupils an addition and subtraction trio such as 11, 6, 5 and ask each one in turn to give a different number sentence which uses these three numbers. Encourage them to listen carefully to what has been said so as not to repeat a sentence. The sentences can be recorded on the board, or on a chart.

■ Focus on the inverse by asking questions such as:
  If 7 + 4 = 11, what is 11 − 4? If 11 − 7 = 4, what is 4 + 7?

Daily Workout Unit 14

Adding 10 to decades

Teaching Tips For Set A

■ Check that pupils can add on 10 to a decade.

■ Discuss commutativity so they realise that, for instance, 10 + 50 = 50 + 10.

Answers

A
- ① 30
- ② 50
- ③ 40
- ④ 60
- ⑤ 30
- ⑥ 90
- ⑦ 70
- ⑧ 60
- ⑨ 70
- ⑩ 80
- ⑪ 90
- ⑫ 100

B
- ① 9
- ② 13
- ③ 17
- ④ 8
- ⑤ 7
- ⑥ 3
- ⑦ 0
- ⑧ 5
- ⑨ 9
- ⑩ 6
- ⑪ 7
- ⑫ 10

C
- ① 7
- ② 4
- ③ 2
- ④ 10
- ⑤ 9

D
- ① Winston
- ② Emily
- ③ Emily
- ④ Kay
- ⑤ Winston

E
- ① Cube
- ② Cylinder
- ③ Cone
- ④ Cuboid

Name _____ Class _____

A

① 20 + 10 .... ④ 50 + 10 .... ⑦ 60 + 10 .... ⑩ 70 + 10 ....

② 40 + 10 .... ⑤ 10 + 20 .... ⑧ 10 + 50 .... ⑪ 10 + 80 ....

③ 10 + 30 .... ⑥ 80 + 10 .... ⑨ 10 + 60 .... ⑫ 90 + 10 ....

B

① 5 + 4 .... ④ 4 + 4 .... ⑦ 5 − 5 .... ⑩ 10 − 2 − 2 ....

② 10 + 3 .... ⑤ 10 − 3 .... ⑧ 8 − 3 .... ⑪ 5 + 4 − 2 ....

③ 7 + 10 .... ⑥ 9 − 6 .... ⑨ 3 + 2 + 4 .... ⑫ 6 + 3 + 1 ....

C

① The sum of 4 and 3 is ....

② The difference between 6 and 2 is ....

③ Eight less than 10 is ....

④ The total of 3, 2 and 5 is ....

⑤ Two more than 7 is ....

D

Name	Number of stickers
Winston	7
Emily	2
George	3
Kay	6

① Who has most? ....

② Who has fewest? ....

③ Who has four fewer than Kay? ....

④ Who has twice as many as George? ....

⑤ Who has four more than George? ....

E

Write the name of each shape.

①

②

③

④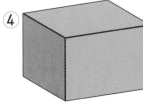

....

Oral Maths

Quick recall of number facts to 20

Pupils sit in groups of between five and ten.

Each group makes a set of Cycle Cards so that each pupil has at least one card. Cycle Cards have a sum on one side and the answer to a different Cycle Card sum on the reverse. Each answer should be a different number.

The sums should include addition and subtraction facts to 20. Pupils can include the addition of more than two numbers in their sums, such as 5 + 3 + 6.

- One child begins by reading the sum on his or her Cycle Card.
- The person who has the answer says *I have the answer which is ...*
- Then that person reads out the sum on the reverse for another pupil to answer.
- This continues until all the sums have been answered.
- The cards are then swapped around amongst the group and the activity repeated.

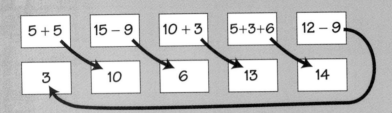

Daily Workout Unit 15

Tens and units

Teaching Tips For Set A

- Check that pupils realise a two digit number is made up of tens and units.
- Encourage pupils to say fifty and six rather than five tens and six units.
  This helps them use the two parts of the number in mental calculations.

Answers

A
  ① 50   ⑤ 80
  ② 40   ⑥ 70
  ③ 30   ⑦ 90
  ④ 60   ⑧ 30

B
  ① 9p   ④ 10p   ⑦ 1p   ⑩ 5p
  ② 11p   ⑤ 8p   ⑧ 5p   ⑪ 8p
  ③ 10p   ⑥ 4p   ⑨ 10p   ⑫ 5p

C
  ① 2   ⑤ 5
  ② 3   ⑥ 8
  ③ 6   ⑦ 2
  ④ 7   ⑧ 2

D ① B   ② A   ③ A   ④ C

E ① 12 o'clock ② 3 o'clock ③ 9 o'clock ④ 6 o'clock

Name .... Class ....

A

Write the missing numbers.

1) $56 = \Diamond + 6$ .... 5) $84 = \Diamond + 4$ ....

2) $42 = \Diamond + 2$ .... 6) $77 = \Diamond + 7$ ....

3) $37 = \Diamond + 7$ .... 7) $95 = \Diamond + 5$ ....

4) $69 = \Diamond + 9$ .... 8) $31 = \Diamond + 1$ ....

B

1) $6p + 3p$ .... 4) $2p + 8p$ .... 7) $5p - 4p$ .... 10) $9p - 4p$ ....

2) $4p + 7p$ .... 5) $10p - 2p$ .... 8) $8p - 3p$ .... 11) $2p + 6p$ ....

3) $5p + 5p$ .... 6) $7p - 3p$ .... 9) $7p + 3p$ .... 12) $7p - 2p$ ....

C

Write the missing numbers.

1) $\Diamond$ more than 4 is 6 .... 5) 2 more than $\Diamond$ is 7 ....

2) $\Diamond$ less than 5 is 2 .... 6) 3 less than $\Diamond$ is 5 ....

3) $\Diamond$ is 1 more than 5 .... 7) 4 is $\Diamond$ more than 2 ....

4) $\Diamond$ is 1 less than 8 .... 8) 8 is $\Diamond$ less than 10 ....

D

Which shape is cut in half?

1) .... 2) .... 3) .... 4) ....

    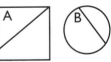

E

Write the times.

1)  2) 3) 4)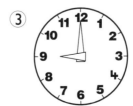

....

Oral Maths

Teen addition facts to 20

0	1	2	3	4	5	6	7	8	9	10

Pupils need to be able to recall or quickly calculate the addition facts to 20 where a single digit is added to a teen number, such as 14 + 5. Techniques pupils can use include:

~ counting on
~ using known facts such as 4 + 5 = 9 to work out 14 + 5 = 19
~ using memory recall.

Each pupil needs a set of Number Cards from the resource sheet on page 62.

They should hold up one or more of their Number Cards in response to activities such as:
Show me the answers to: 13 + 3, 12 + 7, 14 + 5, 6 + 14 ... .
Show me two numbers which total 15 with one of the numbers being more than 10.
14 and which number total 17?

Use the language of addition with activities such as:
Show me 14 plus 6. Show me the total of 3 and 14.
What is the sum of 13 and 5? Show me 4 more than 12. Increase 12 by 6.

Discuss what happens when you add two odd numbers, two even numbers, one of each. Is the answer odd or even?

Daily Workout Unit 16

Addition bonds to 15

Teaching Tips For Set A

■ Pupils should be confident in answering the addition bonds to 15 and have quick recall for most of the bonds.

■ Timing the exercise can help with encouraging quick recall.

Answers

A
① 11	④ 14	⑦ 12	⑩ 14
② 12	⑤ 15	⑧ 12	⑪ 14
③ 13	⑥ 11	⑨ 13	⑫ 13

B
① 10	④ 8	⑦ 8	⑩ 12
② 8	⑤ 3	⑧ 10	⑪ 15
③ 2	⑥ 1	⑨ 11	⑫ 11

C
① 11	⑤ 6
② 2	⑥ 13
③ 9	⑦ 3
④ 6	⑧ 11

D
① 7p	② 10p	③ 6p	④ 3p

E
① Thirty	④ Twenty	⑦ Sixty
② Eighty	⑤ Seventy	⑧ One hundred
③ Forty	⑥ Ninety	⑨ Fifty

A

① 9 + 2 .... ④ 7 + 7 .... ⑦ 9 + 3 .... ⑩ 9 + 5 ....

② 8 + 4 .... ⑤ 9 + 6 .... ⑧ 6 + 6 .... ⑪ 8 + 6 ....

③ 7 + 6 .... ⑥ 7 + 4 .... ⑨ 8 + 5 .... ⑫ 9 + 4 ....

B

① 6 + 4 .... ④ 5 + 3 .... ⑦ 9 – 4 + 3 .... ⑩ 7 + 5 ....

② 10 – 2 .... ⑤ 4 + 2 – 3 .... ⑧ 8 – 2 + 4 .... ⑪ 8 + 7 ....

③ 7 – 5 .... ⑥ 5 + 4 – 8 .... ⑨ 3 + 8 .... ⑫ 6 + 5 ....

C

① Add 6 to 5 .... ⑤ Take away 4 from 10 ....

② 6 take away 4 .... ⑥ Add 3 to 10 ....

③ 7 add 2 .... ⑦ Subtract 7 from 10 ....

④ 8 subtract 2 .... ⑧ 4 add on 7 ....

D

① Ian has 11p.
He spends 4p.
How much is left? ....

② Sean had 5p.
Melanie had twice as much.
How much had Melanie? ....

③ Morgan paid with 10p.
His change was 4p.
How much did he spend? ....

④ Lee had 6p.
Sue had half as much.
How much had Sue? ....

E

Write these numbers in words.

① 30 .... ④ 20 .... ⑦ 60 ....

② 80 .... ⑤ 70 .... ⑧ 100 ....

③ 40 .... ⑥ 90 .... ⑨ 50 ....

Oral Maths

Teen subtraction facts within 20

Pupils need to be able to recall or quickly calculate subtraction facts within 20 where a single digit is subtracted from a teen number to leave a teen number, such as 16 – 3. Techniques pupils can use include:

~ counting back
~ using known facts such as 6 – 3 = 3 to work out 16 – 3 = 13
~ using memory recall.

Each pupil needs a set of Number Cards from the resource sheet on page 62.

They should hold up one or more of their Number Cards in response to activities such as:

Show me the answers to: 19 – 5, 15 – 3, 17 – 4, 20 – 6, ...
The difference between two numbers is 4. The larger number is 16. Show me the other number.
The difference between two numbers is 5. The smaller number is 2. Show me the larger number.

Use the language of subtraction with activities such as:

Show me 19 minus 6. Show me 15 subtract 2. What is 4 less than 17?
What is the difference between 5 and 17? Take away 4 from 20.
Decrease 18 by 6. Subtract 2 from 16.

Discuss what happens when you subtract two odd numbers, two even numbers, one of each. Is the answer odd or even?

Daily Workout Unit 17

Subtraction bonds within 15

Teaching Tips For Set A

■ Pupils should be confident in answering the subtraction bonds within 15 and have quick recall for most of the bonds.

■ Timing the exercise can help with encouraging quick recall.

Answers

A
① 6	④ 5	⑦ 9	⑩ 6
② 5	⑤ 6	⑧ 3	⑪ 8
③ 5	⑥ 7	⑨ 8	⑫ 6

B
① 4	④ 7	⑦ 9	⑩ 4
② 7	⑤ 5	⑧ 10	⑪ 0
③ 5	⑥ 4	⑨ 6	⑫ 2

C
① 3	⑤ 9
② 2	⑥ 6
③ 4	⑦ 8
④ 9	⑧ 6

D
① Jo	② Lisa	③ Lisa
④ Jo	⑤ Lisa and Jo	

E
① 43	④ 61	⑦ 42	⑩ 58
② 36	⑤ 89	⑧ 57	⑪ 48
③ 29	⑥ 95	⑨ 76	⑫ 64

Unit 17

A

1. 11 – 5 ....
2. 12 – 7 ....
3. 15 – 10 ....
4. 13 – 8 ....
5. 12 – 6 ....
6. 13 – 6 ....
7. 11 – 2 ....
8. 11 – 8 ....
9. 14 – 6 ....
10. 15 – 9 ....
11. 15 – 7 ....
12. 14 – 8 ....

B

1. 10 – 6 ....
2. 9 – 2 ....
3. 8 – 3 ....
4. 7 – 0 ....
5. 14 – 9 ....
6. 12 – 8 ....
7. 13 – 4 ....
8. 14 – 4 ....
9. 10 – 3 – 1 ....
10. 9 – 1 – 4 ....
11. 8 – 6 – 2 ....
12. 11 – 3 – 6 ....

C

Write the missing numbers.

1. 11 is 8 more than ◊ ....
2. 12 is 10 more than ◊ ....
3. 11 is 7 more than ◊ ....
4. 15 is 6 more than ◊ ....
5. 6 is ◊ less than 15 ....
6. 5 is ◊ less than 11 ....
7. 4 is ◊ less than 12 ....
8. 8 is ◊ less than 14 ....

D

Name	Amount
Ben	10p
Lisa	3p
Suki	6p
Jo	12p

1. Who has twice as much as Suki? ....
2. Who has 7p less than Ben? ....
3. Who has half as much as Suki? ....
4. Who has 2p more than Ben? ....
5. Which two children have a difference of 9p? ....

E

1. 40 + 3 ....
2. 30 + 6 ....
3. 20 + 9 ....
4. 60 + 1 ....
5. 80 + 9 ....
6. 90 + 5 ....
7. 40 + 2 ....
8. 50 + 7 ....
9. 70 + 6 ....
10. 50 + 8 ....
11. 40 + 8 ....
12. 60 + 4 ....

Oral Maths

Number language

Pupils should sit in a circle and give number sentences about a stated number, such as 18.

Encourage pupils to use a wide range of different types of fact and number language. For example:

Tell me about 18.

- place value and position
    18 is made up of 10 and 8.
    18 is 1 ten and 8 units.
    18 is between 17 and 19.

- addition and subtraction facts
    18 is the sum of 15 and 3.
    18 is the difference between 20 and 2.
    18 is the total of 10, 5 and 3.

- number facts
    18 is an even number.
    18 is not an odd number.
    18 is greater than 14.

Pupils should try not to repeat a number sentence which has been used previously. They should learn to adapt what someone else has said.

Daily Workout Unit 18

Addition bonds to 20

Teaching Tips For Set A

- Pupils should be confident in answering the addition bonds to 20 and have quick recall for most of the bonds.
- Timing the exercise can help with encouraging quick recall.

Answers

A
① 18	④ 19	⑦ 15	⑩ 15
② 15	⑤ 15	⑧ 16	⑪ 14
③ 17	⑥ 20	⑨ 17	⑫ 18

B
① 11p	④ 16p	⑦ 8p	⑩ 10p
② 13p	⑤ 7p	⑧ 8p	⑪ 11p
③ 12p	⑥ 8p	⑨ 17p	⑫ 5p

C ① 15   ② 3   ③ 4   ④ 15   ⑤ 11

D ① 8p   ② 13p   ③ 7p   ④ 9p   ⑤ 10p

E ① half past 3   ② half past 8   ③ half past 1   ④ half past 11

A

① 9 + 9 ....
② 8 + 7 ....
③ 9 + 8 ....

④ 10 + 9 ....
⑤ 9 + 6 ....
⑥ 10 + 10 ....

⑦ 7 + 8 ....
⑧ 8 + 8 ....
⑨ 8 + 9 ....

⑩ 6 + 9 ....
⑪ 7 + 7 ....
⑫ 8 + 10 ....

B

① 4p + 7p ....
② 5p + 8p ....
③ 3p + 9p ....

④ 8p + 8p ....
⑤ 10p – 3p ....
⑥ 15p – 7p ....

⑦ 16p – 8p ....
⑧ 13p – 5p ....
⑨ 10p + 7p ....

⑩ 14p – 4p ....
⑪ 9p + 2p ....
⑫ 13p – 8p ....

C

① The sum of 8 and 7 is ....
② The difference between 9 and 6 is ....
③ Nine less than 13 is ....
④ The sum of 3, 5 and 7 is ....
⑤ Two more than 9 is ....

D

① You have 15p and spend 7p. How much is left? ....
② You have 8p and find 5p. How much have you now? ....
③ You have 12p and lose 5p. How much have you now? ....
④ You have 6p and need 15p. How much more do you need? ....
⑤ You have 20p and spend 10p. How much is left? ....

E

Write the times.

①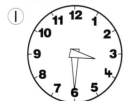

②

③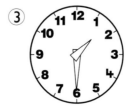

④

....

Oral Maths

Counting in hundreds

Each pupil needs a strip of scrap card, approximately 30 cm long and 5 cm wide which has been divided into 10 parts.

Wind an elastic band around each strip. The elastic band should be sufficiently tight on the strip so that it does not slip up and down.

Before using the strip check that pupils can count forwards and backwards in hundreds to 1000. 'Follow my number on/back' from pages 4 and 6 is a suitable activity for this.

■ Tell pupils that one end of the strip is zero and the other end one thousand. Discuss which number each division mark represents.

■ Ask them to slide the elastic band to show the position of 400 on the strip.
   They should hold up their strips to show their results.

■ Repeat for different hundreds numbers between 0 and 1000.

■ With able pupils discuss the value of the mid-divisions and ask them to show you: 350, 450, 750, ...

■ Decide whether to include counting in thousands from one thousand to ten thousand.

Daily Workout Unit 19

Subtraction bonds within 20

Teaching Tips For Set A

■ Pupils should be confident in answering the subtraction bonds within 20 and have quick recall for most of the bonds.

■ Timing the exercise can help with encouraging quick recall.

Answers

A
① 10	④ 8	⑦ 8	⑩ 6
② 7	⑤ 7	⑧ 7	⑪ 9
③ 8	⑥ 5	⑨ 7	⑫ 9

B
① 15	④ 14	⑦ 9	⑩ 7
② 5	⑤ 4	⑧ 7	⑪ 2
③ 3	⑥ 6	⑨ 8	⑫ 11

C
① 14	⑤ 9
② 8	⑥ 15
③ 10	⑦ 12
④ 9	⑧ 6

D ① 4 g   ② 5 g   ③ 5 g

E ① Cuboid   ② Sphere   ③ Cube   ④ Cylinder

Name .... Class ....

A

① 18 − 8 .... ④ 17 − 9 .... ⑦ 12 − 4 .... ⑩ 13 − 7 ....

② 15 − 8 .... ⑤ 14 − 7 .... ⑧ 16 − 9 .... ⑪ 14 − 5 ....

③ 16 − 8 .... ⑥ 11 − 6 .... ⑨ 12 − 5 .... ⑫ 15 − 6 ....

B

Write the missing numbers.

① 6 + 9 = ◊ .... ④ 7 + 7 = ◊ .... ⑦ ◊ − 2 = 7 .... ⑩ ◊ − 3 = 4 ....

② ◊ + 4 = 9 .... ⑤ 13 − 9 = ◊ .... ⑧ 11 − 4 = ◊ .... ⑪ 8 + ◊ = 10 ....

③ 5 + ◊ = 8 .... ⑥ 10 − ◊ = 4 .... ⑨ 13 − 5 = ◊ .... ⑫ 2 + 9 = ◊ ....

C

① Add together 8 and 6 .... ⑤ Four less than 13 ....

② Subtract 7 from 15 .... ⑥ Six more than 9 ....

③ Total 2, 3 and 5 .... ⑦ Three added to 9 ....

④ Take away 9 from 18 .... ⑧ Eight subtracted from 14 ....

D

① How much heavier is B than A? ....

② A is twice as heavy as B. How heavy is B? ....

③ What is the difference in weight? ....

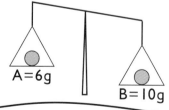

A = 6g   B = 10g

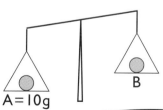

A = 10g   B

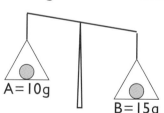

A = 10g   B = 15g

E

Write the name of each shape.

① 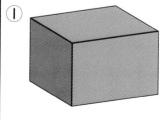 ②  ③  ④

....

Oral Maths

Understanding place value

Each pupil needs a set of Arrow Cards from the resource sheet on page 63.

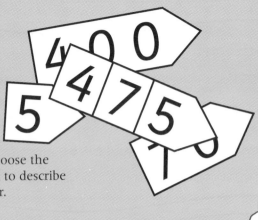

- Ask pupils to put Arrow Cards together to make stated numbers such as:
  Show me: 75, 94, 66, ...
  Show me: 120, 367, 904, ...

- Choose a number such as 378. Ask pupils to choose the Arrow Cards which will make this number and to describe the different ways the cards can be put together.
  378 is 300 and 78.
  378 is 370 and 8.
  378 is 308 and 70.
  378 is 300 and 70 and 8.

- Put the pupils into groups and ask each group member to make a different HTU number. Working as a group they should answers questions such as:
  Who has an even number?
  Who has the number nearest to 200?
  Who has the smallest number?
  Arrange the numbers in order of size.

- Decide whether to extend to thousands.

Daily Workout Unit 20

Totalling coins to 20p

Teaching Tip For Set A

- Pupils should be able to add quickly 1p, 2p, 5p and 10p coins within a total of 20p.

Answers

A
- ① 20p
- ② 17p
- ③ 15p
- ④ 12p
- ⑤ 20p
- ⑥ 19p

B
- ① 16
- ② 10
- ③ 9
- ④ 13
- ⑤ 10
- ⑥ 18
- ⑦ 12
- ⑧ 8
- ⑨ 13
- ⑩ 3
- ⑪ 4
- ⑫ 14

C
- ① 17
- ② 9
- ③ 9
- ④ 12
- ⑤ 11
- ⑥ 9
- ⑦ 13
- ⑧ 6

D
- ① 9p
- ② 8p
- ③ 6p
- ④ A

E
- ① half past 2
- ② half past 12
- ③ half past 7
- ④ half past 4

Name .... Class ....

A

Write the totals.

1. 10p, 10p ....
4. 5p, 5p, 2p ....
2. 10p, 5p, 2p ....
5. 5p, 5p, 10p ....
3. 5p, 5p, 5p ....
6. 2p, 5p, 10p, 2p ....

B

1. 8 + 8 ....
4. 7 + 6 ....
7. 7 + 5 ....
10. 12 − 9 ....

2. 19 − 9 ....
5. 15 − 5 ....
8. 17 − 9 ....
11. 11 − 7 ....

3. 12 − 3 ....
6. 9 + 9 ....
9. 10 + 3 ....
12. 7 + 7 ....

C

1. Eight plus nine ....
5. Total three and eight ....
2. Fifteen minus six ....
6. Subtract two from eleven ....
3. Twelve minus three ....
7. Add four to nine ....
4. Five plus seven ....
8. Take away seven from thirteen ....

D

1. What is the total of stamps B and C? ....
2. What is the difference between stamps A and B? ....
3. How much more is stamp D than stamp B? ....
4. Which stamp is 7p more than stamp C? ....

A **12**p

B **4**p

C **5**p

D **10**p

E

Write the times.

1.

2.

3.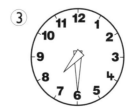

4.

....

Oral Maths

Talking about HTU numbers

Pupils should sit in a circle and give different facts about a stated number, such as 359.

Encourage a wide range of different types of fact. For example:

Tell me about 359.

- place value and position
    359 is three hundreds, five tens and nine units.
    359 is made up of 300 and 59.
    359 is made up of 300, 50 and 9.
    359 is made up of 350 and 9.
    359 is made up of 309 and 50.
    359 is between 358 and 360.

- number facts
    359 is an odd number.
    359 is not an even number.
    359 is greater than 340.

Pupils should try not to repeat a fact which has been used previously.
They should learn to adapt what someone else has said.

Daily Workout Unit 21

Adding small numbers to teen numbers

Teaching Tips For Set A

- Check that pupils can count on by a small number from teen numbers to reach a total.
  The total may occasionally go beyond 20.
- Some pupils may use quick recall or adapt known facts in answering these sums,
  for example, if 9 + 4 = 13 then 19 + 4 = 23.

Answers

A
① 17	④ 18	⑦ 21	⑩ 19
② 17	⑤ 20	⑧ 16	⑪ 23
③ 20	⑥ 21	⑨ 21	⑫ 15

B
① 13	④ 15	⑦ 15	⑩ 12
② 14	⑤ 17	⑧ 16	⑪ 15
③ 16	⑥ 17	⑨ 12	⑫ 15

C
① 17	⑤ 14
② 14	⑥ 17
③ 14	⑦ 21
④ 20	⑧ 17

E
① 30	⑤ 80
② 70	⑥ 30
③ 40	⑦ 50
⑧ 100	⑨ 80

D ① 12p   ② 3p   ③ 5p   ④ 8p

A

① 14 + 3	④ 16 + 2	⑦ 18 + 3	⑩ 14 + 5 ....
② 15 + 2	⑤ 17 + 3	⑧ 12 + 4	⑪ 19 + 4 ....
③ 18 + 2	⑥ 19 + 2	⑨ 16 + 5	⑫ 12 + 3 ....

B

① 4 + 7 + 2	④ 8 + 5 + 2	⑦ 3 + 8 + 4	⑩ 4 + 5 + 3 ....
② 9 + 2 + 3	⑤ 5 + 5 + 7	⑧ 6 + 6 + 4	⑪ 5 + 5 + 5 ....
③ 6 + 6 + 4	⑥ 6 + 3 + 8	⑨ 3 + 2 + 7	⑫ 4 + 2 + 9 ....

C

① 3 more than 14	⑤ Total 3, 5 and 6 ....
② 5 more than 9	⑥ Add together 8 and 9 ....
③ 6 more than 8	⑦ Find the sum of 17 and 4 ....
④ 2 more than 18	⑧ Add 3, 8 and 6 ....

D

① Debra had 6p.
Jay had twice as much.
How much had Jay?   ....

② Reece has 12p.
He spends 9p.
How much is left?   ....

③ Amy had 10p.
John had half as much.
How much had John?   ....

④ Patrick paid with 10p.
His change was 2p.
How much did he spend?   ....

E

Write the missing numbers.

① 10 20 ◊ 40 50	⑤ 90 ◊ 70 60 50 ....
② 40 50 60 ◊ 80	⑥ 50 40 ◊ 20 10 ....
③ 30 ◊ 50 60 70	⑦ 80 70 60 ◊ 40 ....
④ 60 70 80 90 ◊	⑧ 100 90 ◊ 70 60 ....

Oral Maths

Time facts

Check that pupils have a good general knowledge of time facts such as:

- sequence of days and months
    Which day comes before: Monday, Wednesday, Sunday, ... ?
    Which day comes after: Tuesday, Friday, Thursday, ... ?
    Which month comes before: January, March, October, ... ?
    Which month comes after: June, April, December, ... ?

- numerical facts
    How many days in a week?
    How many months in a year?
    How many seasons in a year?
    How many hours in a day?
    How many minutes in an hour?

- general facts
    How many days in a fortnight?
    Which are the weekend days?
    Name me a summer month.
    When is noon?
    When is midnight?

Decide whether to include:

- number of days in a month

- calendar work.

Daily Workout Unit 22

Subtracting small numbers from teen numbers

Teaching Tips For Set A

- Check that pupils can count back by a small number from teen numbers.

- Some pupils may use quick recall or adapt known facts in answering these sums, for example if 7 – 2 = 5 then 17 – 2 = 15.

Answers

A
  ① 12   ④ 15   ⑦ 13   ⑩ 10
  ② 14   ⑤ 11   ⑧ 12   ⑪ 12
  ③ 17   ⑥ 13   ⑨ 11   ⑫ 14

B
  ① 15   ④ 21   ⑦ 10   ⑩ 15
  ② 4   ⑤ 16   ⑧ 16   ⑪ 11
  ③ 4   ⑥ 6   ⑨ 18   ⑫ 7

C
  ① 16   ⑤ 17
  ② 14   ⑥ 19
  ③ 17   ⑦ 12
  ④ 16   ⑧ 23

D
  ① 8   ② 3   ③ 9   ④ 12   ⑤ 3

E
  ① Sphere ② Cone ③ Cube ④ Cylinder

A

① 14 − 2 ....   ④ 17 − 2 ....   ⑦ 19 − 6 ....   ⑩ 14 − 4 ....

② 15 − 1 ....   ⑤ 15 − 4 ....   ⑧ 20 − 8 ....   ⑪ 16 − 4 ....

③ 20 − 3 ....   ⑥ 18 − 5 ....   ⑨ 13 − 2 ....   ⑫ 17 − 3 ....

B

Write the missing numbers.

① $12 + 3 = \Diamond$ ....   ④ $18 + 3 = \Diamond$ ....   ⑦ $\Diamond − 5 = 5$ ....   ⑩ $19 − 4 = \Diamond$ ....

② $\Diamond + 5 = 9$ ....   ⑤ $18 − 2 = \Diamond$ ....   ⑧ $20 − 4 = \Diamond$ ....   ⑪ $\Diamond − 4 = 7$ ....

③ $7 + \Diamond = 11$ ....   ⑥ $7 − \Diamond = 1$ ....   ⑨ $15 + 3 = \Diamond$ ....   ⑫ $10 − \Diamond = 3$ ....

C

① 12 plus 4 ....   ⑤ Total 5 and 12 ....

② 17 minus 3 ....   ⑥ 2 plus 17 ....

③ Add 4 to 13 ....   ⑦ From 17 subtract 5 ....

④ Subtract 3 from 19 ....   ⑧ Add together 5 and 18 ....

D

① Which even number is more than 6 but less than 9? ....

② What is the difference between 13 and 10? ....

③ Total the first three odd numbers. ....

④ Total the first three even numbers. ....

⑤ Halve the third even number. ....

E

Write the names of these shapes.

①   ②    ③    ④

....

Oral Maths

Counting in twos

Pupils sit in a circle and slowly slap the tops of thighs, clap hands then snap fingers – first with one hand then the other. If snapping fingers is difficult then change to wagging a finger on each hand in turn. Continue this to develop a steady rhythm.

■ When the rhythm is steady play 'Count in twos' where you start with any even number. Pupils count on from this number in twos until you say stop.

Thigh	*clap*	*snap*	*snap*	*thigh*	*... .*
Six	*eight*	*ten*	*twelve*	*fourteen*	*... .*

If this creates problems then slow down the actions or allow even more thinking time by counting only on the second snap of fingers.

Decide whether to stop at 20 or to continue beyond.

Between the end of one counting sequence and the start of the next there will be a pause but keep the actions and rhythm going continuously whilst giving further instructions.

■ Start counting on from different numbers.

■ Play 'Silent count' where pupils only say aloud the final snap number and they whisper the thigh, clap and first snap numbers.

■ Tell pupils that they are going to count back in twos. Give them various starting numbers from which to count back.

Daily Workout Unit 23

Finding close differences

Teaching Tips For Set A

■ Pupils should be able to calculate the number difference between a pair of numbers which are quite close together, such as 16 and 14.

■ Discuss counting on and counting back as effective techniques for solving such problems.

Answers

A
① 3	④ 2	⑦ 4	⑩ 4
② 4	⑤ 2	⑧ 3	⑪ 3
③ 4	⑥ 3	⑨ 2	⑫ 4

B
① 16	④ 7	⑦ 5	⑩ 13
② 8	⑤ 17	⑧ 6	⑪ 6
③ 18	⑥ 14	⑨ 5	⑫ 11

C
① 3	⑤ 4
② 3	⑥ 3
③ 3	⑦ 3
④ 3	⑧ 4

D ① Sanjit ② Anita ③ 6 ④ 8

E ① half past 2 ② half past 8 ③ half past 11 ④ half past 4

A Find the differences.

① 20,17 ....   ④ 16,14 ....   ⑦ 16,12 ....   ⑩ 9,13 ....

② 13,17 ....   ⑤ 18,20 ....   ⑧ 13,16 ....   ⑪ 14,17 ....

③ 11,15 ....   ⑥ 19,16 ....   ⑨ 12,10 ....   ⑫ 20,16 ....

B

① $9 + 7$ ....   ④ $15 - 8$ ....   ⑦ $11 - 6$ ....   ⑩ $5 + 8$ ....

② $12 - 4$ ....   ⑤ $8 + 9$ ....   ⑧ $14 - 8$ ....   ⑪ $15 - 9$ ....

③ $9 + 9$ ....   ⑥ $7 + 7$ ....   ⑨ $12 - 7$ ....   ⑫ $4 + 7$ ....

C Write the missing numbers.

① 15 is ◊ more than 12 ....   ⑤ 16 is ◊ less than 20 ....

② 14 is ◊ more than 11 ....   ⑥ 11 is ◊ less than 14 ....

③ 18 is ◊ more than 15 ....   ⑦ 14 is ◊ less than 17 ....

④ 20 is ◊ more than 17 ....   ⑧ 15 is ◊ less than 19 ....

D

Name	Score
Sanjit	17
Jane	9
Anita	7
Kim	15

① Whose score was the highest? ....

② Whose score was the lowest? ....

③ What was the difference between Jane's and Kim's scores? ....

④ How many more did Sanjit score than Jane? ....

E Write the times.

①    ② 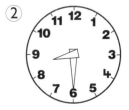   ③ 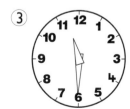   ④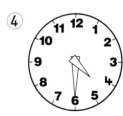

....

Mental Maths *Daily Workout*   **Book 1**

Oral Maths

Counting in tens

Pupils sit in a circle and slowly slap the tops of thighs, clap hands then snap fingers – first with one hand then the other. If snapping fingers is difficult then change to wagging a finger on each hand in turn. Continue this to develop a steady rhythm.

■ When the rhythm is steady play 'Count in tens' where you start with any decade number. Pupils count on from this number in tens until you say stop.

Thigh	clap	snap	snap	thigh	....
Thirty	*forty*	*fifty*	*sixty*	*seventy*	*....*

If this creates problems then slow down the actions or allow even more thinking time by counting only on the second snap of fingers.

Decide whether to stop at 100 or to continue beyond.

Between the end of one counting sequence and the start of the next there will be a pause but keep the actions and rhythm going continuously whilst giving further instructions.

■ Start counting on from different decade numbers.

■ Play 'Silent count' where pupils only say aloud the final snap number and they whisper the thigh, clap and first snap numbers.

■ Tell pupils that they are going to count back in tens. Give them various starting numbers from which to count back.

■ Include counting forwards and back in twos.

Daily Workout Unit 24

Calculating change from 20p

Teaching Tip For Set A

■ Pupils should be able to calculate the change required from 20p using a range of techniques which include:
  ~ counting on
  ~ counting back
  ~ quick recall of known facts.

Answers

A
① 5p ④ 17p ⑦ 6p
② 8p ⑤ 13p ⑧ 12p
③ 9p ⑥ 15p ⑨ 11p

B
① 11 ④ 17 ⑦ 13 ⑩ 5
② 15 ⑤ 15 ⑧ 4 ⑪ 6
③ 19 ⑥ 18 ⑨ 19 ⑫ 14

C
① 20 ⑤ 13
② 5   ⑥ 16
③ 14 ⑦ 17
④ 1   ⑧ 19

D
① Saturday ② Saturday and Sunday
③ 14 ④ 7 ⑤ 12

E
① Square ② Triangle ③ Cube ④ Cylinder

Name .... Class ....

A

Write the change from 20p.

① 15p .... ④ 3p .... ⑦ 14p ....

② 12p .... ⑤ 7p .... ⑧ 8p ....

③ 11p .... ⑥ 5p .... ⑨ 9p ....

B

① 15 − 4 .... ④ 8 + 9 .... ⑦ 8 + 5 .... ⑩ 13 − 8 ....

② 17 − 2 .... ⑤ 18 − 3 .... ⑧ 11 − 7 .... ⑪ 12 − 6 ....

③ 16 + 3 .... ⑥ 9 + 9 .... ⑨ 15 + 4 .... ⑫ 7 + 7 ....

C

① The total of 6 and 14 is .... ⑤ 15 minus 2 is ....

② 8 less than 13 is .... ⑥ The total of 8 and 8 is ....

③ The sum of 8 and 6 is .... ⑦ 13 plus 4 is ....

④ The difference between 13 and 14 is .... ⑧ The sum of 4 and 15 is ....

D

① Which day follows Friday? ....

② Which two days are in a weekend? ....

③ How many days in a fortnight? ....

④ How many days in a week? ....

⑤ How many months in a year? ....

E

Write the names of these shapes.

①  ②  ③ 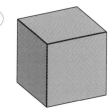 ④

....

Oral Maths

Counting in fives

Play 'Fizz-buzz-bang'

■ Pupils count forward in unison, at a steady rate. When they reach 5 or a multiple of 5, they should say 'buzz' instead of the number word.
One, two, three, four, buzz, six, seven, eight, nine, buzz, eleven, ...

■ Continue the activity, except this time when they reach 2 or a multiple of 2 they say 'fizz'.
One, fizz, three, fizz, five, fizz, seven, fizz, nine, fizz, eleven, ...

■ Repeat except that on 10 or multiples of 10 pupils say 'bang'.

■ Extend the activity to counting backwards.
Forty-seven, forty-six, buzz, forty-four, forty-three, ...
Seventeen, fizz, fifteen, fizz, thirteen, fizz, ...
Sixty-two, sixty-one, bang, fifty-nine, fifty-eight, ...

■ For a real challenge bring the activities together so that multiples of both 2 and 5 become 'fizz-buzz'.
One, fizz, three, fizz, buzz, fizz, seven, fizz, nine, fizz-buzz, eleven, ...
If appropriate repeat for other combinations of 'Fizz-buzz-bang'.

Daily Workout Unit 25

Totalling coins to 50p

Teaching Tips For Set A

■ Pupils should be able to quickly add 5p, 10p and 20p coins within a total of 50p.

■ The ability to count in fives and tens obviously helps.

Answers

A ① 35p ④ 35p
⁢ ② 40p ⑤ 45p
⁢ ③ 30p ⑥ 40p

B ① 5 ④ 8 ⑦ 4 ⑩ 3
⁢ ② 10 ⑤ 4 ⑧ 3 ⑪ 8
⁢ ③ 7 ⑥ 7 ⑨ 0 ⑫ 10

C ① 15 ② 17 ③ 13 ④ 22 ⑤ 18

D ① 9p ② 15p ③ 5p, 2p, 2p ④ 2p, 2p, 1p

E ① February ④ July ⑦ April
⁢ ② September ⑤ March ⑧ December
⁢ ③ June ⑥ October ⑨ August

Name ....   Class ....

A Write the totals.

1. 10p, 10p, 10p, 5p   ....
2. 10p, 10p, 10p, 10p   ....
3. 20p, 10p   ....
4. 20p, 10p, 5p   ....
5. 20p, 20p, 5p   ....
6. 20p, 10p, 10p   ....

B Write the missing numbers.

1. $5 + \Diamond = 10$ ....
2. $\Diamond - 7 = 3$ ....
3. $9 - \Diamond = 2$ ....
4. $\Diamond + 2 = 10$ ....
5. $5 + \Diamond = 9$ ....
6. $\Diamond - 1 = 6$ ....
7. $4 - \Diamond = 0$ ....
8. $6 + \Diamond = 9$ ....
9. $\Diamond + 2 = 2$ ....
10. $\Diamond - 3 = 0$ ....
11. $2 + \Diamond = 10$ ....
12. $\Diamond - 4 = 6$ ....

C

1. The difference between 19 and 4 is   ....
2. The sum of 13 and 4 is   ....
3. Three less than 16 is   ....
4. Four more than 18 is   ....
5. The total of 3 and 15 is   ....

D

1. Martin has 7p.
   Alison has 2p more.
   How much has Alison?   ....

2. Steven has 6p.
   Liz has 3p more.
   How much have they altogether?   ....

3. Michael has 3 coins.
   The total is 9p.
   What are the three coins?   ....

4. Sally has 3 coins.
   The total is 5p.
   What are the three coins?   ....

E Write which months follow these.

1. January   ....
2. August   ....
3. May   ....
4. June   ....
5. February   ....
6. September   ....
7. March   ....
8. November   ....
9. July   ....

Oral Maths

The 2× table

Each pupil needs a set of Number Cards from the resource sheet on page 62.

Remind pupils that, for instance 3×2 gives the same answer as 2×3. Encourage quick recall of the table facts.

■ Play 'Show me' activities where pupils hold up a Number Card in response to multiplication problems.

Show me the answer to: 2×5, 2×6, 2×10, 2×3, ...
Show me the answer to: 5×2, 6×2, 10×2, 3×2, ...
Show me the answer to: 8×2, 2×8, 2×5, 7×2, ...
What is double: 4, 6, 9, 8, ... ?

■ Work from the answer back.

Show me two numbers which multiplied together make: 12, 18, 10, 8, ...

■ Discuss the fact that all the answers are even numbers.

Daily Workout Unit 26

Doubling numbers

Teaching Tips For Set A

■ Pupils should be able to recall the doubles of small numbers.

■ Discuss the fact that whole numbers which are doubled give even answers.

Answers

A ① 4   ④ 10   ⑦ 12
      ② 6   ⑤ 14   ⑧ 20
      ③ 8   ⑥ 18   ⑨ 16

B ① 12   ④ 12   ⑦ 17   ⑩ 15
      ② 8   ⑤ 16   ⑧ 14   ⑪ 11
      ③ 11   ⑥ 6   ⑨ 11   ⑫ 11

C ① 19   ⑤ 19
      ② 13   ⑥ 5
      ③ 12   ⑦ 17
      ④ 17   ⑧ 16

D ① 31   ② 30   ③ February   ④ 52   ⑤ 12

E ① half past 5   ② half past 11   ③ half past 8   ④ half past 1

Unit 26

A

Double each number.

① ② ....   ④ ⑤ ....   ⑦ ⑥ ....

② ③ ....   ⑤ ⑦ ....   ⑧ ⑩ ....

③ ④ ....   ⑥ ⑨ ....   ⑨ ⑧ ....

B

① 4 + 3 + 5 ....   ④ 7 + 7 − 2 ....   ⑦ 14 + 6 − 3 ....   ⑩ 13 − 2 + 4 ....

② 7 + 2 − 1 ....   ⑤ 15 + 4 − 3 ....   ⑧ 12 − 4 + 6 ....   ⑪ 15 − 1 − 3 ....

③ 6 − 3 + 8 ....   ⑥ 13 − 9 + 2 ....   ⑨ 12 + 3 − 4 ....   ⑫ 17 − 3 − 3 ....

C

① Add 3 to 16 ....   ⑤ 16 plus 3 ....

② 18 minus 5 ....   ⑥ From 13 subtract 8 ....

③ Total 4, 2 and 6 ....   ⑦ Add together 3 and 14 ....

④ 4 plus 13 ....   ⑧ Subtract 4 from 20 ....

D

① How many days are in January? ....

② How many days are in June? ....

③ Which month has fewer days than April? ....

④ How many weeks in a year? ....

⑤ How many months in a year? ....

E

Write the times.

①    ②    ③ 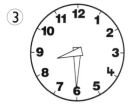   ④

....

Mental Maths *Daily Workout*   **Book 1**

Oral Maths

The 10× table

Recall of the 10× tables does not usually cause many problems. Remind pupils that, for instance, 10×2 gives the same answer as 2×10. Encourage quick recall of the table facts.

Each pupil needs the Arrow Cards from the resource sheet on page 63.

- Play 'Show me' activities where pupils hold up Arrow Cards in response to multiplication problems.
   Show me the answer to: 10×4, 10×7, 10×10, 10×5, ...
   Show me the answer to: 6×10, 4×10, 2×10, 9×10, ...
   Show me the answer to: 7×10, 10×8, 5×10, 10×2, ...

- Work from the answer back.
   Show me two numbers which multiplied together make: 50, 90, 20, 70, ...

Discuss the fact that all answers in the 10× table end in zero.

Daily Workout Unit 27

Halving numbers

Teaching Tips For Set A

- Pupils should be able to recall the halves of small numbers.
- Discuss the fact that they are only halving even numbers.

Answers

A
- (1) 2
- (2) 4
- (3) 3
- (4) 6
- (5) 7
- (6) 10
- (7) 5
- (8) 9
- (9) 8

B
- (1) 12p
- (2) 7p
- (3) 13p
- (4) 17p
- (5) 12p
- (6) 19p
- (7) 15p
- (8) 16p
- (9) 11p
- (10) 2p
- (11) 15p
- (12) 6p

C
- (1) 14
- (2) 6
- (3) 13
- (4) 20
- (5) 11
- (6) 12
- (7) 8
- (8) 5

D
- (1) 12
- (2) 17
- (3) 19
- (4) 11
- (5) 21

E
- (1) Cuboid
- (2) Sphere
- (3) Rectangle
- (4) Hexagon

Name	Class

A

Halve each number.

① 4 ....   ④ 12 ....   ⑦ 10 ....

② 8 ....   ⑤ 14 ....   ⑧ 18 ....

③ 6 ....   ⑥ 20 ....   ⑨ 16 ....

B

① 5p + 7p ....   ④ 14p + 3p ....   ⑦ 6p + 9p ....   ⑩ 11p − 9p ....

② 13p − 6p ....   ⑤ 15p − 3p ....   ⑧ 8p + 8p ....   ⑪ 18p − 3p ....

③ 20p − 7p ....   ⑥ 17p + 2p ....   ⑨ 4p + 7p ....   ⑫ 18p − 12p ....

C

① Double 7 ....   ⑤ Double 4 add 3 ....

② Halve 12 ....   ⑥ Halve 6 add 9 ....

③ 16 subtract 3 ....   ⑦ Double 6 subtract 4 ....

④ 14 add 6 ....   ⑧ Halve 14 subtract 2 ....

D

① What is the difference between half of 16 and 20? ....

② What is the total of double 7 and 3? ....

③ What is the sum of 8, 7 and 4? ....

④ What is half of 18 subtracted from 20? ....

⑤ What is double 6 added to half of 18? ....

E

Write the names of these shapes.

① 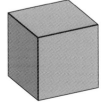   ②    ③    ④

....

Mental Maths *Daily Workout*   **Book 1**

Oral Maths

The 5× table

Remind pupils that, for instance, 6 × 5 gives the same answer as 5 × 6. Encourage quick recall of the table facts.

Each pupil will need to cut out 10 equilateral triangles – using a 2D shape as a template will be helpful.

They write one 5× table fact on each triangle like this:

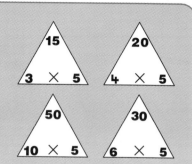

Pupils work in small groups of twos and threes. They take turns to cover up any one of the three corner numbers with their thumb and ask their partner which number is hidden. The answer is checked by removing the thumb.

Encourage covering up different corners so that it is not always the answer to the multiplication which is covered.

Daily Workout Unit 28

Totalling coins to £1

Teaching Tips For Set A

■ Pupils should be able to quickly add 5p, 10p, 20p and 50p coins within a total of £1.

■ The ability to count in fives and tens obviously helps.

Answers

A
  ① 60p   ④ 75p
  ② 70p   ⑤ £1
  ③ 70p   ⑥ 65p

B
  ① 20   ④ 17   ⑦ 15   ⑩ 11
  ② 13   ⑤ 21   ⑧ 7   ⑪ 13
  ③ 7   ⑥ 11   ⑨ 20   ⑫ 18

C
  ① 16   ⑤ 16
  ② 21   ⑥ 17
  ③ 17   ⑦ 14
  ④ 14   ⑧ 15

D
  ① 21p   ② 16p   ③ 11p   ④ C   ⑤ 5p

E
  ① half past 5 ② half past 2 ③ half past 7 ④ half past 12

Name .... Class ....

A

Write the totals.

① (20p), (20p), (20p) .... ④ (50p), (10p), (10p), (5p) ....

② (20p), (20p), (20p), (10p) .... ⑤ (50p), (20p), (20p), (10p) ....

③ (50p), (20p) .... ⑥ (50p), (10p), (5p) ....

B

① 18 + 2 .... ④ 8 + 9 .... ⑦ 7 + 8 .... ⑩ 16 − 5 ....

② 17 − 4 .... ⑤ 15 + 6 .... ⑧ 12 − 5 .... ⑪ 15 − 2 ....

③ 16 − 9 .... ⑥ 20 − 9 .... ⑨ 17 + 3 .... ⑫ 9 + 9 ....

C

① The difference between 20 and 4 .... ⑤ Halve 8 add 12 ....

② The total of 3, 6 and 12 .... ⑥ Double 4 add 9 ....

③ The sum of 8, 4 and 5 .... ⑦ Double 10 subtract 6 ....

④ The difference between 16 and 2 .... ⑧ Halve 18 add 6 ....

D

① What is the total of B and C? ....

② What is the difference between A and D? ....

③ How much more is B than A? ....

④ Which stamp is 9p less than B? ....

⑤ What is the difference between B and D? ....

A **4**p

B **15**p

C **6**p

D **20**p

E

Write these times.

①    ②    ③ 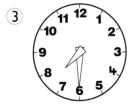   ④

....

Mental Maths record sheet

	Oral Maths		Daily Workout Focus	
1	Counting on		Addition bonds to 10	
2	Counting back		Subtraction bonds within 10	
3	Quick recall of addition facts to 10		Totalling coins to 10p	
4	Quick recall of subtraction facts within 10		Pairs which total 10	
5	Addition and subtraction trios		Totalling three numbers	
6	Quick recall of number facts to 10		Inverse of addition	
7	Telling the time – o'clock and half past		Solving equations of the type $3 + \Diamond = 8$	
8	Counting in tens		Solving equations of the type $\Diamond + 1 = 8$	
9	Talking about TU numbers		Inverse of subtraction	
10	Counting on		Solving equations of the type $7 - \Diamond = 2$	
11	Counting back		Solving equations of the type $\Diamond - 2 = 5$	
12	Addition facts to 20		Mixed addition and subtraction	
13	Subtraction facts to 20		Adding 10 to digits	
14	Addition and subtraction trios		Adding 10 to decades	
15	Quick recall of number facts to 20		Tens and units	
16	Teen addition facts to 20		Addition bonds to 15	
17	Teen subtraction facts within 20		Subtraction bonds within 15	
18	Number language		Addition bonds to 20	
19	Counting in hundreds		Subtraction bonds within 20	
20	Understanding place value		Totalling coins to 20p	
21	Talking about HTU numbers		Adding small numbers to teen numbers	
22	Time facts		Subtracting small numbers from teen numbers	
23	Counting in twos		Finding close differences	
24	Counting in tens		Calculating change from 20p	
25	Counting in fives		Totalling coins to 50p	
26	2× table		Doubling numbers	
27	10× table		Halving numbers	
28	5× table		Totalling coins to £1	

Mental Maths pupils record sheet

Name

Unit	Set A	Set B	Set C	Set D	Set E	Self-assessment
1						
2						
3						
4						
5						
6						
7						
8						
9						
10						
11						
12						
13						
14						
15						
16						
17						
18						
19						
20						
21						
22						
23						
24						
25						
26						
27						
28						

Number Cards

Cut out the number cards.

0	1	2	3	4
5	6	7	8	9

1	2	3	4	5
6	7	8	9	10
11	12	13	14	15
16	17	18	19	20

Arrow Cards

1 0 6 | 1 0 0
2 0 8 | 2 0 0
3 0 7 | 3 0 0
4 0 9 | 4 0 0
5 0 5 | 5 0 0
6 0 4 | 6 0 0

0 0 7 0 | 0 0 8 0 | 0 0 6 0
0 3 0 | 0 2 0 | 0 1 0
7 | 8 | 6

0 0 0 5 | 6 0 0 0
0 0 0 4 | 7 0 0 0
0 0 0 3 | 8 0 0 0
0 0 0 2 | 9 0 0 0
0 0 0 1

Clock Face